Compute
This!

JiM DAViS

ℛℛ
RAVETTE PUBLISHING

First published by Ravette Publishing 2003.

Printed and bound in Great Britain
for Ravette Publishing Limited,
Unit 3, Tristar Centre,
Star Road, Partridge Green,
West Sussex RH13 8RA
by Cox & Wyman Ltd, Reading, Berkshire

ISBN: 1 84161 194 8

NEVER HELP ME WITH THE LAUNDRY AGAIN!

LET'S HEAR IT FOR INCOMPETENCE

www.garfield.com

SCRATCH
SCRATCH

THAT WAS QUITE A BURST OF ACTIVITY

I HOPE NOBODY GOT HURT

www.garfield.com

JIM DAVIS 11-2

JiM DAViS 11-3

www.garfield.com

JIM DAVIS 11-9

OTHER GARFIELD BOOKS AVAILABLE

Pocket Books		Price	ISBN
Below Par		£3.50	1 84161 152 2
Bon Appetit		£3.50	1 84161 038 0
Eat My Dust		£3.50	1 84161 098 4
Fun in the Sun		£3.50	1 84161 097 6
The Gladiator		£3.50	1 85304 941 7
Gooooooal!		£3.50	1 84161 037 2
Great Impressions		£3.50	1 85304 191 2
I Don't Do Perky	(new)	£3.50	1 84161 195 6
In Training		£3.50	1 85304 785 6
The Irresistible		£3.50	1 85304 940 9
Light Of My Life		£3.50	1 85304 353 2
On The Right Track		£3.50	1 85304 907 7
Pop Star		£3.50	1 84161 151 4
To Eat, Or Not To Eat?		£3.50	1 85304 991 3
Wave Rebel		£3.50	1 85304 317 6
With Love From Me To You		£3.50	1 85304 392 3

Theme Books	Price	ISBN
Guide to Behaving Badly	£4.50	1 85304 892 5
Guide to Cat Napping	£4.50	1 84161 087 9
Guide to Coffee Mornings	£4.50	1 84161 086 0
Guide to Creatures Great & Small	£3.99	1 85304 998 0
Guide to Healthy Living	£3.99	1 85304 972 7
Guide to Pigging Out	£4.50	1 85304 893 3
Guide to Romance	£3.99	1 85304 894 1
Guide to Successful Living	£3.99	1 85304 973 5
Guide to The Seasons	£3.99	1 85304 999 9

2-in-1 Theme Books		Price	ISBN
The Gruesome Twosome		£6.99	1 84161 143 3
Out For The Couch		£6.99	1 84161 144 1
Easy Does It	(new)	£6.99	1 84161 191 3
Licensed to Thrill	(new)	£6.99	1 84161 192 1

Classics		Price	ISBN
Volume One		£5.99	1 85304 970 0
Volume Two		£5.99	1 85304 971 9
Volume Three		£5.99	1 85304 996 4
Volume Four		£5.99	1 85304 997 2
Volume Five		£5.99	1 84161 022 4
Volume Six		£5.99	1 84161 023 2
Volume Seven		£5.99	1 84161 088 7
Volume Eight		£5.99	1 84161 089 5
Volume Nine		£5.99	1 84161 149 2
Volume Ten		£5.99	1 84161 150 6
Volume Eleven	(new)	£5.99	1 84161 175 1
Volume Twelve	(new)	£5.99	1 84161 176 X

Little Books		Price	ISBN
Food 'n' Fitness		£2.50	1 84161 145 X
Laughs		£2.50	1 84161 146 8
Love 'n' Stuff		£2.50	1 84161 147 6
Wit 'n' Wisdom		£2.50	1 84161 148 4
C-c-c-caffeine	(new)	£2.50	1 84161 183 2
Surf 'n' Sun	(new)	£2.50	1 84161 186 7
The Office	(new)	£2.50	1 84161 184 0
Zzzzzz	(new)	£2.50	1 84161 185 9

Miscellaneous			
Garfield 25 years of me!		£7.99	1 84161 173 5
Treasury 4	(new)	£10.99	1 84161 180 8
Treasury 3		£9.99	1 84161 142 5
21st Birthday Celebration Book		£9.99	1 85304 995 6

All Garfield books are available at your local bookshop or from the publisher at the address below. Just tick the titles required and send the form with your payment to:-

RAVETTE PUBLISHING
Unit 3, Tristar Centre, Star Road, Partridge Green, West Sussex RH13 8RA

Prices and availability are subject to change without notice.
Please enclose a cheque or postal order made payable to **Ravette Publishing** to the value of the cover price of the book and allow the following for UK postage and packing:

60p for the first book + 30p for each additional book
except *Garfield Treasuries* and *21st Birthday Celebration Book* . . . when please add £3.00 per copy for p&p

Name ....

Address ....

....

....

....